In the early 1930's, when th.   m grip on the nation, the glass industry started mass proaucʀon of "tank" glass, now known to a growing number of collectors as Depression Glass. Some patterns date back to the 1920's, a few were hand-molded from "pot" glass, but the bulk of Depression Glass being sought out today was machine-molded.

Huge volumes of liquid glass flowed through pipes connected to a string of automatic pressing molds. By this relatively new technique, large quantities of glassware could be turned out in one operation.

Color was everywhere—no doubt to offset the gray pall of "hard times". A palette of colors was used in the production of Depression Glassware; a myriad of pinks, blues, greens; deep tones of cobalt, burgundy, amethyst; plus frosted colors, milk translucents, and opaques. Clear (often called "crystal") was made in very small quantities in comparison with the abundance of glassware produced. Today, clear is a "sleeper" on the market.

Manufacturers, furniture and appliance stores, theaters, gasoline stations, all used this colorful glassware as premiums to promote their products and services. The Shirley Temple milk pitcher, cereal bowl, and mug, so popular with Depression Glass collectors today, were packed in General Mills cereals.

The colored glassware in this book sold originally for as little as 3 cents a piece, and all the way up to an outrageous 99 cents. S. S. Kresge, Sears & Roebuck, many department stores, and other five-and-dime stores offered four place-settings (twenty pieces) for only $1.99. In its country-wide chain, S. S. Kresge sold nearly 100 carloads of the "Miss America" pattern in less than a year.

The elaborate pattern designs in much of the Depression Glass were not simply decorative, but were used to cover up imperfections in the glass. Many pieces will have dents, ripples, and mold lines, but nevertheless are considered mint condition.

In comparison with the large volume of colored glassware sold and given away during this era, only a trickle of it is showing up in second-hand and antique stores today. Much of the glass was thin and brittle, not able to withstand extremes of heat and cold, so breakage accounts for a huge loss. In the more affluent 1940's, people began pushing this inexpensive glass to the back of their cupboards, or packing it away in attics and basements.

The intrinsic worth of Depression Glass, so much a part of our heritage, is just dawning on collectors and homemakers. As its popularity spreads, collecting it can be an exciting Treasure Hunt. This colored glassware is so decorative and versatile, everyone should own at least a piece or two as a memento of our past.

PLATE ONE

Sportsman Series. Patterns in this series were made by the Hazel Atlas Glass Co. Outdoor sports inspired the various motifs of the sets. The decorations are fired on, over either cobalt or clear glass. Full sets are available. *Sportsman Series* is of good quality, deep cobalt, and rounded shape. *Wedding Band* is an excellent fill-in for this pattern.

ROW I—1. Sailboat tumbler.
     2. Hunt shaker, no shaker lid.
     3. Sailboat pie plate, 6".
     4. Windmill shaker w/lid, strainer spout.
     5. Golf tumbler with Hazel Atlas mark on bottom.

Hairpin. A pattern not previously listed, *Hairpin* comes in a rainbow of colors. Coloring is the same as *Wedding Band,* and the two patterns compliment each other. The *Hairpin* lines are pressed into the glass, edges on the plates are slightly scalloped, and centers are always plain, rounded; average quality.

ROW II—1. Cobalt sugar.
     2. Cup, milk, almost opaque.
     3. Cobalt luncheon plate.
     4. Amethyst creamer.

Wedding Band. From Hazel Atlas, the H astride the A appears on the bottom of some of these pieces. If this banded pattern is your choice, the *Hairpin* or *Sportsman Series* above will make excellent fill-in pieces for your set. Centers are plain, with horizontal bands encircling each piece, 1934 to 1937.

ROW III—1. Cobalt salt shaker with H/A mark.
     2. Amethyst creamer, scarce.
     3. Cobalt butter with metal cover, plastic knob.
     4. Cobalt sugar.

Pink Hobnail and Opalescent (Moonstone) Hobnail. Anchor-Hocking introduced the *Pink Hobnail* in 1936, and their *Opalescent Hobnail* in 1938 under the *"Moonstone"* name. They could still be purchased in department stores in 1960's. Both Duncan & Miller and Fenton carried the pattern under *"Hobnail"* in the 1940's. The Anchor-Hocking *Hobnail* has a many-rayed star in relief in the center and/or on the feet of their pattern, whereas neither Duncan & Miller nor Fenton's have it. Refer to *The Glass Rainbow* by Johana Anderton and *Forties Revisited* by James Lafferty, Sr. for further comparison.

ROW IV—1. Opalescent tiny creamer.
     2. Pink sherbet with liner.
     3. Puff box with cover (makes excellent butter box).
     4. Salt and pepper shakers, probably Duncan & Miller, note hobnail on base instead of rayed star.

PLATE TWO

Fruits. Made by Jeannette and several other glass companies of the 1920-1930's in various shapes; from poor to good quality, depending on the glass manufacturer.

ROW I—1. *Cherry* sherbet, stem footed, light green, poor quality.
   2. *Fruits* luncheon plate, medium green, average quality, seams rough.
   3. *Fruits* pitcher, heavy, good quality, mint green, lemon depicted on one side, orange on the other.

ROW II—1. *Banded Fruits* tumbler, 5″, pale pink, good quality.
   2. Jeannette's *Cherry Spray* beverage pitcher, medium green, good quality.
   3. *Fruits* candleholder, rosy pink, fruits in high relief, excellent quality, nice fill-in for *Cherry* collections, also.

Panelled Cherry Blossom. Jeannette Glass Co., available in hues shown, plus clear and salmon pink. The pinks vary in this pattern, so be sure to detect the difference between salmon pink (orange-hued or brownish) and deep rosy pink (lavender) (shown).

ROW III—1. Cone tumbler, 4″, footed, blue opaque, called "Delfite".
   2. Butter dish with lid, deep rosy pink.
   3. Beverage pitcher, footed, medium mint green.

Banded Cherry. Jeannette Glass Co., known to date only in medium green, clear, and pinks.

ROW IV—1. Tumbler, 4″.
   2. Cone beverage pitcher, footed.
   3. Juice tumbler.

The era of this glass is just dawning. Antique dealers tend to group the *Cherry, Cherry Spray, Panelled Cherry* and *Banded Cherry* all under one name, *"Cherry Blossom"*, so know your pattern well, especially if you are collecting this pattern through the mail-order media.

PLATE THREE

Basket. Indiana Glass Co. sold this as their *"Lorain"* line. This pattern was made in a beautiful lemon yellow, as well as clear, opaque white, and mint green. It was produced in only 14 pieces. The heavy-footed stem tumbler is a variation of the original *"Lorain"* line and, to date, has been seen only in green or pink, 1929-1932.

ROW I—1. Lemon yellow creamer.
2. Lemon yellow platter, 11½".
3. Heavy-footed stem goblet variation, deep mint green, 5¼".

Poppy Family. There are three variations of this pattern. *Ruffled Poppy, Poppy #1* (slightly scalloped), and *Poppy #2* (rounded). All come in lemon yellow, pale pink, clear, and mint green, plus a rich cobalt blue that is scarce. Note the difference in handles on the patterns. *Ruffled Poppy* appears to have the *Poppy #2* handles. All three variations can be used in the same setting, as the basic floral design is the same. Also called *Florentine,* 1932-1936.

Ruffled Poppy.

ROW II—1. Clear creamer.
2. Pale pink comsommé with handles.
3. Open sugar, clear.

Poppy #1.

ROW III—1. Pale pink 9" serving bowl.
2. Lemon yellow *Poppy #2* (rounded edges) condiment tray with *Poppy #1* (scalloped edges) creamer, sugar with lid, salt and pepper.

Poppy #2.

ROW IV—1. Lemon yellow footed cocktail glass (note difference between sherbet shown).
2. Lemon yellow gravy boat with kidney shape meat platter.
3. Lemon yellow stem sherbet, footed.
4. Mint green frappé, 6", used by some collectors as a vase.

PLATE FOUR

Miss America. Hocking Glass Co. distributed this line in the late 1920's and early 1930's. The star ray centers in this pattern are uniform in circle. In elongated pieces, such as platters, the rays form an elongated oval. The bases of sherbets and other stemmed pieces are square. The glass is not as heavy as its sister pattern, *English Hobnail,* nor is the cut as deep, but *English Hobnail* is a wonderful fill-in for this pattern.

English Hobnail. Westmoreland Glass Co. produced this pattern by a hand-mold process. It was machine-made by other glass manufacturers. The hobnails are deep-cut on heavy glass. The bases are generally round on salts and on stemmed items. The star ray centers in *English Hobnail* are always 6-sided, even on cup bottoms. Note cup handle also differs in design from *Miss America.*

ROW   I—1. *Miss America* apple green cup.
      2. *English Hobnail* clear luncheon plate, notice 6-sided star ray center.
      3. *English Hobnail* clear cup.

ROW   II—1. Mint green *English Hobnail* salt shaker.
      2. *Miss America* clear salt shaker, note square base.
      3. *Miss America* deep rosy pink compote with lid.
      4. *English Hobnail* rose pink nut dish with card holder, origin unknown.
      5. *English Hobnail* milk glass salt shaker.

ROW III—1. *Miss America* apple green candleholder.
      2. *English Hobnail* open compote, cone shape, footed, deep mint green.
      3. *English Hobnail* flat creamer, deep mint green.

ROW IV—1. *Miss America* deep rose pink butter dish. Without the lid, it is a cereal bowl. The distributor sent seperate tops so bowls could be sold as either butter dishes or cereals.
      2. *Miss America* clear bon-bon server with central metal handle.
      3. *English Hobnail* milk glass individual salt dish.
      4. *English Hobnail* robin's egg blue salt dish.
      5. *English Hobnail* deep dish nappy, flared, mint green.

PLATE FIVE

Parrot. Federal Glass Co. made this pattern in a bright mint green, as well as in amber. They also made the less abundant round-shaped *Parrot* in a thinner glass. New collectors tend to confuse this with the *Lovebird* pattern. *Parrot* is well defined, shows three large parrots full length, perched under tropical leaves. There are no baskets in the *Parrot* pattern as in *Lovebird*. Made for six months only, 1932.

    ROW I—1. *Parrot* creamer, bright mint green.
          2. *Parrot* salt shaker, square base.
          3. *Parrot* 9″ dinner plate.
          4. Thin-blown *Parrot* tumbler.

Lovebird. Federal Glass Co. issued their *Lovebird* pattern for four years, starting in 1931, and in light mint green only. Extra accessory pieces are not available. Also promoted as *Georgian* this pattern is on the upswing in value. A pair of lovebirds, set in a large V, alternate with baskets, and are connected by a rope drape. The thin-blown tumblers do not have the lovebirds, only baskets. The salt shakers have a thin band of flowers that matches the edges of other pieces in this pattern.

    ROW II—1. *Lovebird* creamer, footed.
          2. *Lovebird* stem sherbet.
          3. *Lovebird* 4″ shell tumbler, baskets only.
          4. *Lovebird* sugar bowl with lid.

Dolphin. Hazel Atlas, as well as McKee Glass Co., produced *Dolphin* items. *Dolphin* candleholders date back to Sandwich Glass 1840 and McKee 1860, and have been reproduced ever since. The large fish boat comes in blue milk by McKee and frosty clear by U.S.A. Glasbake. Where you find the glasswear of the twenties and thirties, you usually will find pieces of U.S.A. Glasbake.

    ROW III—1. Light green small *Dolphin* candleholder.
          2. Large frosty clear fish boat.
          3. Large true pink *Dolphin* candleholder.

Bluebird. Origin unknown at present, produced in the early thirties.

    ROW IV—1. True pink *Bluebird* console dish.
          2. Small *Bluebird* vase with frog insert in light green, available from yellow-green (almost vasoline) to black amethyst.
          3. Swan console dish, mint green, originally used for calling cards.

PLATE SIX

Ribbon. This pattern is characterized by a raised narrow panel in high relief between each ribbon, and always has a rounded ray base. Tumblers, plus sugar and creamers, are cone-shaped. Available in light green and milk glass. Hazel Atlas, 1930-1931.

ROW I—1. *Ribbon* candy dish with lid, stem, footed.
2. Light green 8½″ deep bowl.
3. *Ribbon* cup.

Cabbage Rose. The *Cabbage Rose* series was fashioned after the original Pattern Glass *Cabbage Rose* made in 1881 for the San Francisco Exposition. It was also advertised as *Sharon,* but *Cabbage Rose* seems more descriptive to some collectors. Full sets are available in it, plus two variations, *Cabbage Rose* with triple arches and *Cabbage Rose* with single arch (Anderton's *Dutch Rose*). *Cabbage Rose* w/triple arch has scalloped edges on almost all flat pieces. This series comes in crystal clear, mint green, yellow amber, and true pink. All pieces mix well with sister patterns for decorative settings.

Cabbage Rose with arch (Anderton's *Dutch Rose*.) Federal's *Rosemary,* 1935-1936.

ROW II—1. Yellow amber 4¼″ tumbler.
2. Yellow amber 12″ platter, lightly scalloped.
3. Mint green cup and saucer.

Cabbage Rose (Anderton's *Sharon*) Federal's *Sharon* 1935-1939.

ROW III—1. Yellow amber flat salt shaker.
2. Yellow amber butter dish with wide brim.
3. Mint green candy compote, stem footed.

Cabbage Rose with triple arch. Federal's *Mayfair,* 1934.

ROW IV—1. Yellow amber cup and saucer.
2. Clear 12″ scalloped platter.
3. Yellow amber 4¼″ tumbler, heavily arched.

PLATE SEVEN

Stippled Rose Band. Macbeth-Evans allegedly introduced this pattern at about the same time as their *Dogwood* pattern. *Stippled Rose Band* is a delicate pattern on almost shell-thin glass. The colors are extremely pale, almost clear. A striking pattern, it looks lovely on a lace tablecloth of a pastel hue.

ROW I—1. Creamer, clear with light apricot stain band.
2. Pale yellow, almost clear, cup and saucer.
3. Sugar bowl, matches creamer.

Dogwood. Macbeth-Evans is credited with *Dogwood*. However, apparently they promoted it under the name of *Appleblossom*. The possibility also exists that this is not their pattern at all, and that perhaps they did issue an *Appleblossom* pattern similar to this. The flower on the *Dogwood* series has only four petals, with a half round bite out of each petal, and can only be a dogwood flower. Appleblossoms have five petals and are somewhat more ruffled. This has caused much confusion with collectors. *Dogwood* is a very delicate pattern on thin glass.

ROW II—1. Mint green saucer with pale pink cup.
2. Frosted dogwoods on shell beverage pitcher.
3. Pale pink creamer.

Wildrose with Appleblossoms. This pattern is of unknown origin, dating from the late 1920's into the 1930's. The color is a true pink, very good glass, similar decor as that of the *Dogwood* series.

ROW III—1. True pink candleholder, frosted on the wildrose and appleblossom, double ring.
2. Oblong tray, for either dining room or dresser.
3. True pink candleholder, frosted on the wildrose and appleblossom, no double ring. It may be interesting to note that #1 and #3 in this row were purchased from the original owner as a pair.

Wildflower. This has an interesting motif, a myriad of wildflowers, snowflake-like flowers, and leaves, almost like an intaglio, cut on the underside of the glass. To date, this pattern has been seen in frosted aqua, clear, amber, and burgundy. The glass is of average quality and the shapes are diamonds and squares. Indiana Glass Co., 1932-1937.

ROW IV—1. Frosted aqua diamond compote.
2. Clear tray with filigree frame.
3. Amber cream soup.

PLATE EIGHT

The vertical and horizontal rib patterns have confused both collectors and dealers more than any other patterns in the glass field. The rib sizes and styles vary so much, this is one area where we must go by description.

Horizontal Rounded Big Rib. The ribs on this pattern are large and well-rounded, not sharp to the touch at all. It makes an excellent fill-in for *Horizontal Sharp Big Rib* shown in Row IV. Notice that the light does not refract from this as it does from the *Horizontal Sharp Big Rib*.

> ROW I—1. Pale pink cookie jar with clear lid.
> 2. Pink three-legged candy dish.
> 3. Pale pink salt shaker.
> 4. Small tipped beverage pitcher, clear.

Double Shield. This is characterized by the shield in relief design on the sides of cups, bowls, and undersides of plates. On handled items, the shield is where the handles attach. A good quality glass, it comes in black amethyst, two shades of colbalt, clear, and burgundy. The handles on this pattern always have the elongated scroll S. The double candleholders have a beaded (raised) band encircling the bottom edge as well as the shield. Edges are scalloped on plates, sugar and creamers.

> ROW II—1. Cobalt creamer.
> 2. Deep cobalt bowl.
> 3. Black amethyst tray with center handle.

Horizontal Threads with Triple Horizontal Band. This is copied from the old Pattern Glass *Threaded* pattern. The Depression pattern is characterized by three large, rounded, horizontal ribs, then uniform horizontal threading. Of good quality glass, it makes a striking table decor.

> ROW III—1. Mint green open sugar, footed.
> 2. True pink sandwich server.
> 3. Mint green creamer.

Horizontal Sharp Big Rib. This pattern has large well-defined horizontal ribs, not rounded, but rather sharp. It gives marvelous light reflection and makes a handsome fill-in for any pattern of heavy glass. Anchor-Hocking's *Manhattan* pattern, 1939.

> ROW IV—1. Clear stem wine, 3¾".
> 2. Salmon pink tumbler, 5¼", footed.
> 3. Clear 8" bowl, also comes with metal handle attached to tabs.
> 4. Clear creamer.

PLATE NINE

Spoke. This pattern was advertised in the Sears & Roebuck Catalogue of 1933 without a name. Amber seems to be the most prevalent color. The center-spoke decor is quite large and fills the centers of plates, saucers, etc. This set also features an 11″ dinner plate. Tumblers are shell-thin and of average quality.

ROW I—1. Footed 5″ yellow amber tumbler.
      2. Divided dinner plate, 11″, bright mint green.
      3. Clear salt and pepper shakers.

Paneled Aster. A striking set, shown in lemon yellow, the pattern alternates panels with groups of asters, leaves, and lattice, in low raised relief. Origin at this time is unknown, probably early 1930's. Quality is average, the glass being a little heavier than most, and the tumblers are as heavy as the other pieces.

ROW II—1. Lemon yellow creamer.
      2. Footed tumbler, 5½″.
      3. Lemon yellow sugar, matches creamer.

Cameo-Ballerina. Presently one of the most popular patterns, this comes in an assortment of colors; clear, bright mint green, green frosted, bright emerald green, pink, and lemon yellow. Sometimes it is decorated with a gold or platinum band around the rim edge. Most covers and lids do not carry the ballerina pattern on them, so one must be aware of the tiny features of this pattern when collecting whole sets. Items pictured are the hardest to find and the 7″ milk pitcher is the most scarce. Quality is average, but the pattern has many eye-appealing pieces. Hocking Glass Co., 1930.

ROW III—1. Footed stem sherbet, bright mint green.
      2. Clear tumbler with platinum band, 4½″.
      3. Low candy dish with gold band encircling rim.
      4. Milk pitcher, 7″, bright mint green.

ROW IV—1. Bright mint green single candleholder.
      2. Bright mint green creamer or syrup with drip tray.
      3. Lemon yellow 6″ champagne, stemmed, footed.

PLATE TEN

Royal Lace. Hazel Atlas Glass Co. sold this pattern through the Sears & Roebuck catalogue and other media. An exceptionally popular pattern, it is most abundant in pink, clear, green, cobalt, and rarely in amethyst. *Royal Lace* has candleholders in three styles, fruit bowls in two styles. Prices are based on popularity of the moment and the law of supply and demand. Flat pieces are slightly scalloped.

ROW   I—1. Cobalt 13″ oval platter, 1936.
             2. Large bowl, 1936.

ROW   II—1. Mint green open sugar bowl, footed, 1934.
             2. Cobalt beverage pitcher with ice guard, 1936.
             3. Pale pink 4″ tumbler, 1934.
             4. Cobalt sundae dish with metal holder, 1936.

ROW III—1. Cobalt tall footed creamer, 1936.
             2. Amethyst cookie jar, no lid, 1937.
             3. Cobalt single candleholder, 1936.
             4. Cobalt sugar bowl with lid, 1936.

Kitchen Items. McKee made many kitchen items during this period, mostly in the lightly marbled opaque milk glass. The rainbow of colors offered will compliment all of the myriad hues of the period.

ROW IV—1. Blue milk orange squeezer.
             2. Large tab-handled bowl, upside to show design, marked McKee *"Panelled Scroll"*.
             3. Blue milk measuring cup set, some fire on rim.

PLATE ELEVEN

Frosted Block. Indiana Glass Co. produced this in the late 1920's and early 1930's, and apparently production was continued through 1940 in various colors. The set is quite nice and a little different from other straight line patterns. Colors are yellow amber, pale pink, light green, carnival, and clear.

ROW I—1. Light green footed creamer.
2. Light green luncheon plate.
3. Pale pink cream soup with handles.

Cloverleaf. This pattern comes in pale yellow, light green, the pale pinks, and the blacks; black amethyst, black amber, and black opaque. In the black family, black opaque is the most common. However, all black is somewhat scarce. Note shapes are the same as the *Ribbon* pattern (Plate Six). Hazel Atlas, 1931.

ROW II—1. Black opaque salt and pepper shakers, footed.
2. Light green candy dish with lid.
3. Black opaque creamer.
4. Black opaque open sugar, footed.

Knife and Fork. Hocking Glass Co. A heavy glass with huge sugar and creamer, this is the largest of all Depression glassware. There are many diversities of this pattern, the forks having two, three, or four tines, and the knife blade varying. This is another pattern copied from the original Pattern Glass. Many extra pieces are available, and the pattern should be a challenge to collect.

ROW III—1. True pink sugar bowl with lid.
2. True pink spoon holder.
3. True pink cream pitcher.

ROW IV—1. Small stemmed goblet, light green.
2. Stemmed wine goblet, 4".
3. Jigger, mint green.
4. *Feather Scroll* true pink creamer.
5. Amethyst six-sided cup and saucer, made by U. S. Glass Co. and others.

PLATE TWELVE

Buttons & Bows. This line was promoted by Jeannette Glass Co. as *Holiday*. However, collectors still tend to call it *Buttons & Bows* which is self-descriptive. The glass is heavy and rather bulky to stack.

ROW I—1. Milk pitcher, 4½″ tall, true pink.
   2. Round cake tray, 10½″, no legs.
   3. Butter dish with lid, true pink.
   4. True pink tumbler, 4″.

Sunflower, Thistle, and Many Windows patterns. The *Sunflower* cake plate that is so abundant was a Swans Down flour premium. *Thistle* is attributed to Macbeth & Evans and is shaped like its sister pattern, *Dogwood*. Hocking Glass Co. produced *Many Windows* in 1936.

ROW II—1. Pale pink *Sunflower* cone tumbler, footed.
    2. McKee opaque milk-green lemon squeezer.
    3. Pale green *Thistle* thin 8″ luncheon plate.
    4. *Many Windows* stem sherbet, footed, with liner.
    Shown in yellow green, also made in pale pink.

Poinsettia and Adam. These patterns were made by Jeannette Glass Co., in true pink and mint green. The styles are similar in both patterns; the glasses and pitchers are cone-shaped, candleholders are the same shape, and both sets offer a covered casserole. *Poinsettia* is sometimes called *Floral,* but with over one hundred floral patterns available, plus a daily stream of new collectors and dealers, the title *Floral* leads only to confusion. 1932-1934.

Poinsettia

ROW III—1. True pink refrigerator tray, 6″ square.
    2. True pink cinnamon-sugar or spice shaker.
    3. Mint green stemmed candy dish with lid.
    4. True pink divided relish dish.
    5. Mint green salt shaker.

Adam

ROW IV—1. Mint green candleholder.
    2. Mint green salt dish, will compliment any pattern.
    3. Covered casserole, true pink.
    4. Covered candy dish or rose bowl, true pink.

Elongated Honeycomb. Many companies made a honeycomb pattern of some type; some more elongated than others, some with the comb on the inside, others on the outside, of the item. This particular pattern has a horizontal honeycomb strip encircling the piece about one to two inches from the rim, to break the overall honeycomb pattern.

ROW I—1. Footed tumbler, 4½", medium mint green.

    2. Large water pitcher, medium mint green.

    3. Medium mint green salt shaker, salmon pink salt shaker.

Iris And Herringbone. Jeannette Glass Co. issued this pattern in an assortment of items. This is another pattern copied from the old Pattern Glass. There are variants in the pattern itself, so probably several companies produced it. The glass is heavier than most of your Depression Glass, and comes in round and rippled shapes. This pattern was still being sold in the 1950's. The motif is in semi-high relief with stippled rays of panels stopping only at the iris.

ROW II—1. Marigold tumbler, 6", footed.

    2. Clear candy dish, covered, with tab handles.

    3. Marigold sherbet, footed.

Hazel Atlas Honeycomb. Hazel Atlas Glass Co. made thousands of the *Honeycomb* items for the "Shirley Temple" pieces found in General Mills food products at the time. The front side shows the picture of Shirley Temple and is smooth, the honeycombs resuming on each side of the picture.

Georgian. This is a classic pattern, still being made today in several variations. The glasses and pitchers are good fill-ins for other patterns. The tumbler shown is the same style that Hocking Glass Co. produced in 1935.

ROW III—1. Shirley Temple mug, back side.

    2. Cobalt *Georgian* 4" tumbler.

    3. Large *Georgian* water pitcher with ice guard, medium mint green.

    4. Shirley Temple milk pitcher, front side.

Cube. Jeannette Glass Co. produced *Cube* in the 1933 era. There is a similar pattern, *American,* issued by Fostoria, that has polished bottoms and is heavier. Care should be taken not to confuse the two qualities and patterns. Amber (not yellow amber) and avocado are new and being marketed today, but the quality is not the same as the 1920 pattern.

ROW IV—1. Bright mint green 3" creamer, also made in a 2" creamer.

    2. Covered butter dish, bright mint green.

    3. Covered three-legged candy dish, true pink.

    4. Bright mint green tumbler, 4".

Doric and Doric With Pansy. Jeannette Glass Co. Both patterns are extremely sought after, and it is difficult to complete a set. *Doric* is a snowflake pattern in individual squares alternating with plain squares. In the *Doric With Pansy* pattern, the alternating squares have a pansy in full bloom. The *Doric With Pansy* pattern also has a child's set. Both patterns are comparatively scarce. The pitcher shown is the only size to come to light thus far.

ROW   I—1. Medium mint green pitcher, 6″ fat, *Doric*.
         2. Medium mint green *Doric* square tray, 8x8″, which can accomodate four square inserts (see Row II, #4).
         3. *Doric* bowl with flared rim, 8″, medium mint green.

ROW   II—1. Blue milk cloverleaf condiment server.
         2. *Doric With Pansy* oval serving platter with tab handles, teal blue.
         3. *Doric* salt shaker, medium mint green.
         4. *Doric* true pink individual server, fits into square tray shown in row above.

ROW III—1. *Doric* coaster, true pink.
         2. *Doric With Pansy* cake platter, teal blue.
         3. *Doric* cup and saucer, true pink.
         4. *Doric* blue milk footed stem sherbet.

ROW IV—1. *Doric With Pansy* sherbet cup and liner, teal blue.
         2. Large serving bowl, *Doric With Pansy*, tab handles, teal blue.
         3. *Doric With Pansy* cup and saucer, teal blue.

Thorn. Heretofore unlisted, *Thorn* is the same shape as many *Cameo* pieces. *Cameo* also has a bowl shaped like the one pictured; however, it is scarce. The *Thorn* berry server and individual berry bowls are three-legged. The center of the bowl has many thorny branches. Glass is rather heavy and good quality.

Flower Rim. An early 1930 pattern, the decor of flowers and leaves is on the rim only. Often the pattern is marked "Vitrock" on the underside. The opaque white has a bluish cast, and sometimes pale blue marble lines will be seen. Quality is somewhat poor, as items are off-center and lopsided.

> ROW I—1. *Thorn* berry server, three legged, bright mint green.
> 2. *Flower Rim* 9″ dinner plate.

Windsor Diamond. Jeannette Glass Co. produced this line in the 1930's. The highlight of the pattern is a canoe-shaped serving bowl. Aside from the usual colors of this period, the pattern also comes in a deep emerald green and a bluish clear, but both colors are scarce.

> ROW II—1. Milk pitcher, clear, 5″.
> 2. Canoe serving boat, true pink.
> 3. Large beverage pitcher, bright mint green.
> *(Also see Row IV, #3)*

Bowknot. *Bowknot* is found in only a few pieces. These could be collected for a luncheon set or as a fill-in pattern. Light mint green is the only color seen thus far. The pattern is characterized by dainty bows looped between flowers on a medium thin glass.

> ROW III—1. Berry bowl, 4″ diameter.
> 2. Scalloped plate, 7″ diameter.
> 3. Footed sherbet.
> 4. Footed 5″ tumbler.

Pinwheel. The glass of *Pinwheel* is thinner than most of these patterns. About fifteen different items were made, so that one can complete a basic set or use it as a fill-in pattern. The green is exceptional in this pattern, particularly when it picks up light refractions.

> ROW IV—1. Covered butter dish, true pink.
> 2. *Pinwheel* deep bowl, 8½″ round, bright mint green.
> 3. *Windsor Diamond* cup, bluish clear.
> 4. *Pinwheel* footed salt shaker, true pink.

PLATE SIXTEEN

Open Rose (Mayfair). This pattern features many different items and therefore has wide appeal to collectors of whole sets. It comes in rainbow colors—frosted pink, clear, apple green, azure blue, true pink. Some pieces have hand-painted flowers on them. The Hocking Glass Co. advertised this as their *Mayfair* line in 1931. However, *Open Rose* seems more self-descriptive to collectors.

Gothic Arches. This pattern comes in true pink, amber, medium mint green, and clear. The arches overlaced in high relief from a cobweb-like motif.

ROW I—1. *Open Rose* footed ice tea tumbler, azure blue.

2. *Open Rose* wide decanter with stopper, true pink.

3. *Open Rose* whiskey jigger, true pink.

4. *Gothic Arches* amber dessert plate, 7½".

5. *Gothic Arches* candleholder, medium mint green.

6. *Open Rose* juice or milk pitcher, clear.

ROW II—All *Open Rose* pattern.

ROW II—1. Azure blue stem goblet, 6" high.

2. Salt and pepper shakers, azure blue.

3. Footed candy compote, frosted pink, enamelled flowers on lid.

4. Azure blue sherbet cup with liner.

Madrid. Many companies made *Madrid* under various names, such as *Meandering Vine, Primus,* and *Winged Medallion.* Azure blue is hard to find in some areas, and pink is generally scarce.

ROW III—1. Flat bottomed salt shaker, medium mint green.

2. Footed salt shaker, medium mint green.

3. Amber sherbet cup with underliner. Underliner has off-center depression that cup fits into; probably used as a "cookies and ice cream" set.

4. Azure blue serving bowl, large.

5. Square pitcher, 8", amber.

ROW IV—1. Kellogg's cereal bowl, light mint green; issued as a premium with Kellogg's cereals.

Starlight. Hazel Atlas, 1936-1938. It comes in cobalt, clear, pink, and green. Heavy glass, good quality.

ROW IV—2. *Starlight* round bowl, 8", tab handles.

Banded Ribbon. This pattern is quite similar to *Ribbon,* except for the horizontal band that encircles each piece. This set is of the 1920's and has a covered casserole dish. The glass is of average quality, and the pattern has been seen only in medium mint green.

ROW IV—3. *Banded Ribbon* footed salt shaker.

4. Footed sugar bowl.

5. Footed wine or cordial.

PLATE SEVENTEEN

Children's Dishes. Children's sets in Depression Glass are always popular, and the demand far outstrips the supply. Akro Agate manufactured children's sets in clear, opaques, and marbled opaques. Most sets are marked, and were produced in all Depression colors.

ROW   I—1 & 2. Child's light green lemonade pitcher and tumbler (from a complete set).

        3. Child's cup and saucer, cobalt.

        4. Federal's *Diana—Swirled Sharp Rib* miniature cup and saucer set, clear, shown in original storage frame. This set came with the original label, has miniature dinner plates (not shown) to match, clear with gold band.

        5 & 6. Child's cobalt *Block* lemonade tumbler and pitcher.

ROW   II—1 & 5. Child's matched teal blue *Basket* sugar and creamer.

        2. *Doric With Pansy* cup and saucer, deep rosy pink.

        3. *Diana—Swirled Sharp Rib* flashed ruby red cup and saucer.

        4. *Iris and Herringbone* child's cup and saucer, or demitasse, clear.

        5. See #1 above.

ROW   III—1. *Cherry Blossom* sugar and creamer in pink.

        3. Child's creamer, pitcher, and sugar in pink opaque.

        4, 5, & 6. *Cherry* cup and saucer, creamer, sugar, in blue opaque, called "Delfite".

Stemware. Shown in Row IV is an assortment of stemware, mostly Fostoria, made for the adult sets. Stemware is hard to collect, as there are so many styles and variations. It was produced in every color and usually of shell-thin glass.

ROW   IV—1. *Quilted Diamond* pale pink wine goblet.

        2. Footed water goblet, about 5".

        3. Pastel green stem goblet, 7".

        4. Jigger set, burgundy, green, and salmon pink, metal holder.

        5. Pale pink stem champagne or sherbet.

        6. Stem water goblet, drape-effect design, 7".

        7. Stem champagne or sherbet, 5", rich mint green.

PLATE EIGHTEEN

Ribbon Candy. A striking set, *Ribbon Candy* originated from the ever popular Bryce-McKee pattern. It comes in clear and has a unique feature in that the flat soup bowls and luncheon plates each possess a tab handle. This set was also made with a stippled background and the *Ribbon Candy* pattern overlaid in high relief. Bases are usually square, and the line is of good quality glass.

ROW I—1. Soup bowl, 7″.
2. Cup and saucer set.
3 & 4. Matched creamer and sugar, on small pedestals.

Christmas Candy. This set comes in teal blue, as well as clear and emerald green. Origin is the Indiana Glass Co., and is dated 1936. *Christmas Ribbon Candy* is a more descriptive name for this pattern. It is of good quality glass and seems to be scarce. Items apparently were made for luncheon sets only.

ROW II—1 & 3. Matched sugar and creamer on *Christmas Candy* base.
2. Pie plate, 6″.
4. *Petal Swirl* variant, kitchen salt shaker with indent for label.

Open Lace (Anderton's *Lace Edge*). Another Hocking Glass Co. line, vintage 1935-38, advertised as their *Lace Edge*. Cups and tumblers in this pattern are not easily identified because no lace appears on them, just the vertical rays. Centers of all covers and lids are rayed. Candleholders are in two styles. All pieces shown are in pale true pink.

ROW III—1. Candy compote with lid, stem footed.
2. Single candleholder.
3. Covered butter dish.
4. Cup, note vertical rays, no lace.

Banded Fine Rib. Like many patterns of this era, *Banded Fine Rib* descended from an old Pattern Glass style. Hocking Glass Co., 1936.

ROW IV—1. Pale true pink 6″ pie plate.
2. Individual berry bowl, 5″, sitting atop 9″ round serving bowl, burgundy.
3. Bright mint green basket centerpiece to compliment any of the green patterns. Comes in all Depression Glass colors.

PLATE NINETEEN

Comet. A poor quality glass (as in *Fruit* pattern), *Comet* comes in pale green. Believed to be from the U. S. Glass Co., early 1920's, luncheon pieces are available (See Row I, #1).

Shaggy Daisy. This is by the U. S. Glass Co. Center is beaded, with much scroll design in the overall pattern (See Row I, #2).

Stippled Tree of Life. Many companies issued a Tree of Life pattern; some plain, some stippled, or entwined with snow flakes. Shown is an early 1930 version (See Row I, #4). Imperial Glass Co.

American Sweetheart. A most popular pattern, the glass is very thin and fragile. As well as the standard colors of pink, green, and clear, it comes in the unusual colors of white opalescent with smoky blue trim, cobalt, true red, and milk opalescent with gold trim. The latter colors are quite scarce and collectible. (See Row I, #3 and all of Row II).

ROW I—1. *Comet* 6" pie plate, light mint green.
2. *Shaggy Daisy* 3-legged cake plate, true pink.
3. *American Sweetheart* frosty clear sundae dish.
4. *Stippled Tree of Life* single candleholder, true pink.

ROW II—All pieces are *American Sweetheart.*

ROW II—1. Footed sugar bowl, true red.
2. Cup and saucer, true red.
3. Luncheon plate, 9", true red.
4. White opalescent footed salt shaker.
5. White opalescent footed creamer, smoke trim.

Sandwich Family. *Sandwich* is another pattern with many names and much confusion. A host of companies produced this popular pattern, with many variants, across a span of years. Westmoreland's *Princess Feather* pattern has a zig-zag band at the top, plus an intricate "H" design; two characteristics unique from other *Sandwich* patterns (See ROW III, #1 and #5). The *Oatmeal Lace* patterns (known by many as conventional *Flower*) are of heavier glass than other *Sandwich* patterns (See Row III, #4 and #6, and Row IV, #4).

ROW III—1. Westmoreland's *Princess Feather* flat salt shaker.
2. *Early American Sandwich* (by Indiana Glass Co.) wine decanter, clear. (Stopper is an Avon product).
3. *Early American Sandwich* 3 oz. stem wine goblet.
4. *Oatmeal Lace* covered butter dish, peacock blue.
5. *Princess Feather* footed salt shaker, clear.
6. *Oatmeal Lace* 5" bowl, scalloped edge, burgundy.

Petal (Anderton's *Diamond Point*). By Jeannette Glass Co., this is a thin glass in pale pink, clear, cobalt, and milk. Some pieces have added decorations. In 1937, Sears & Roebuck advertised a 32-piece set of *Petal* for $2.49!

ROW IV—1. *Petal* mayonnaise or honey cup with attached liner.
2. *Petal* 8" luncheon plate, milk with gold floral decor.
3. *Sandwich* lime green 8" luncheon plate.
4. *Oatmeal Lace* sherbet cup and liner, emerald green.

PLATE TWENTY

Kitchen Items. Every glass manufacturer, of course, made many kitchen items. In comparison with the volume produced, little has made it through the era. The glass quality was not the best, and items had constant use.

ROW I—1. Syrup pitcher with tin lid, Hazel Atlas, medium mint green.
2. Measuring cup with reamer insert, pale true pink.
3. Four-cup measurer, medium mint green, Jeannette Glass Co.
4. Footed salt and pepper shakers, jade green.

Pyramid. This is a three-sided tiered-effect pattern of good quality. Cambridge is credited with producing this in the early 1920's. Accessory pieces compliment many patterns as fill-ins.

ROW II—1. Kitchen item, salesman sample salt and pepper shakers, tin lids.
2 & 4. Pair of *Pyramid* single candleholders in medium mint green.
3. *Pyramid* frosted pink vase.
5. Kitchen item, salesman sample salt and pepper shakers with glass lids, true pink.

Flute. This is another classic pattern produced in variants by many companies. Shown here is Federal's *Flute*. Flutes vary with the piece, from seven to ten flutes, with scalloped edge. The pattern seems to be most abundant in the greens.

ROW III—1. *Flute* coaster, medium mint green.
2. Individual berry bowl with five-sided rayed center.
3. Seven-flute heavy beverage pitcher, bright mint green.
4. *Flute* candleholder with finger loop, medium mint green.
5. Federal's advertising ashtray, true amber.

Oyster & Pearl. This set is collectible in burgundy, pink, and clear, with pink the most prevalent. Heisey made this pattern in quality glass with ground polished bottoms. There are only about six items in this pattern, all serving or accessory pieces.

ROW IV—1. Kitchen item, utility ash tray with insert for matchbox, bright mint green.
2. *Oyster & Pearl* one-handled nappie or candy dish, burgundy. 1939, Anchor-Hocking Co.
3. *Oyster & Pearl* fruit bowl, 11″ diameter, salmon pink.
4. Kitchen item, utility butter dish, covered, bright mint green.

PLATE TWENTY-ONE

Bouquet & Lattice. (Anderton's *Normandie*). Federal Glass Co. introduced this line in 1933 and continued it into the 1940's. Even though Federal listed this pattern as *Normandie, Bouquet & Lattice* seems more descriptive to some collectors. The glass is thin. In certain parts of the country, amber and green are rarely seen now.

ROW I—1. Flat salt shaker, yellow amber.
        2. Pale pink tumbler, 4", shell thin.
        3. Yellow amber tumbler, 5".
        4. Footed short stem sherbet, yellow amber.
        5. Pale pink cup.

Princess. A square-shaped pattern, *Princess* has been attributed, thus far, to the Hocking Glass Co. The pattern has a drape and tassel effect, and is presently gaining in popularity. Princess has six color hues, all pastel.

ROW II—1. Spice shaker, light mint green (scarce).
        2. Lemon yellow salt shaker.
        3. Oblong platter, tab handles, light mint green.
        4. Juice pitcher, 6", light mint green (scarce).

Horseshoe. This pattern was sold through the Sears and Roebuck Catalogue in 1931. Also, Indiana Glass Co. sold this as *No. 612*. The shape is the same as many pieces of *Daisy*. The lemon yellow in this pattern is quite exquisite and will increase in value.

ROW III—1. Footed tumbler, 9 oz., lemon yellow.
        2. Footed creamer, square pedestal, mint green.
        3. Divided relish tray, three legs, bright mint green.
        4. Lemon yellow sugar bowl, square pedestal.

Old Cafe. Only about fifteen pieces in this pattern are known, making it a good fill-in for other patterns. Centers are rayed and, like *Open Lace*, the tumblers have vertical rays. However, the *Old Cafe* tumblers have a center star and beaded rim on the bottoms.

ROW IV—1. Open candy dish, burgundy.
        2 & 3. Juice tumblers, 3", pale true pink. Note beading on upside-down tumbler.
        4. *Oyster & Pearl* burgundy candleholder. (See Plate Twenty, Row IV, #2 and #3).

PLATE TWENTY-TWO

Windowpane. A product of Hazel Atlas Co., most pieces of *Windowpane* are marked with the HA. The glass is quite heavy and bulky. The vertical lines are in high relief, broken by horizontal panes. This set goes well with Colonial decor and presently is a "sleeper" on the market.

Sunburst. Jeannette Glass Co. issued *Sunburst* in 1938 through 1940. This set has an eleven-inch dinner plate, and, to date, has been seen only in clear.

    ROW I—1. *Windowpane* footed stem sherbet, medium mint green.

          2. *Sunburst* footed creamer, clear.

          3. *Windowpane* candy compote with lid.

          4. *Windowpane* creamer, clear.

Flat Diamond. This pattern should not be confused with similar Cambridge or Heisey patterns that have ground bottoms. *Flat Diamond* was introduced in the 1920's in an array of pastel colors.

    ROW II—1. One-handled cream soup bowl.

          2. *Flat Diamond* stem sherbet with underliner, true pink.

          3. Miscellaneous salt. Tulip basket, medium mint green.

          4. *Flat Diamond* stem sherbet, medium mint green.

Fine Rib. Pink, clear, and cobalt appear to be the only colors in this set. With vertical ribbing as the basic design, a waffle motif covers the centers of butter dishes, plates, etc. However, the waffle design is not on every piece in the set. Many collectors tend to confuse *Fine Rib* with the pattern *Homespun*. *Homespun* (not pictured in the book) has both vertical and horizontal lines in its basic design, just like the weave in homespun material.

    ROW III—1. *Fine Rib* covered butter dish, pale pink.

          2. Footed sugar bowl, no lid.

          3. Miscellaneous salt. Clear basket.

          4. *Fine Rib* 3″ juice tumbler, cobalt.

          5. *Horizontal Fine Rib* covered jam compote. Placed beside *Fine Rib*, this shows that if you fused the vertical lines of *Fine Rib* and the lines of *Horizontal Fine Rib*, you would have the pattern *Homespun*.

Vertical Big Rib. Some collectors have thought this was Heisey's *Crystolite* pattern; however, it is not. Heisey's *Crystolite* is a much finer quality glass, has more brilliance, and has a ground bottom. There were no patents on glass patterns in this era, and most Depression Glass styles were copies. For comparison, Row IV shows the Heisey Ice Bucket (#3) next to *Vertical Big Rib* to show the clarity and brilliance of the true Heisey.

    ROW IV—1. *Vertical Big Rib* 4″ tumbler, pale pink.

          2. *Vertical Big Rib* pale pink creamer.

          3. Heisey *Crystolite* signed ice bucket, tab handles.

          4. *Vertical Big Rib* sherbet cup with underliner.

PLATE TWENTY-THREE

Swirled Sharp Rib (Anderton's *Diana*). This pattern has caused more confusion than it should, particularly between *Swirled Sharp Rib (Diana)* and *Swirled Big Rib*. Both patterns are shown here for comparison. The ribs in *Swirled Sharp Rib (Diana)* are sharp to the touch, whereas those in *Swirled Big Rib* are rounded. Many glass companies manufactured the ribbed series. *Swirled Sharp Rib (Diana)* was made by Federal Glass Co., while *Swirled Big Rib* was produced by Imperial Glass Co., among others. *Swirled Sharp Rib (Diana)* is shown in miniature on the children's page (Plate Seventeen).

ROW I—All pieces are *Swirled Sharp Rib (Diana)*.

ROW I—1. Yellow amber creamer.
    2. Pale pink two-handled consomme.
    3. Yellow amber salt shaker.
    4. Yellow amber sugar bowl, matches #1.
    5. Pale pink ashtray.

Petal Swirl. This set comes in teal blue (shown) and a peacock blue (with greenish cast), plus pink. Glass is of average quality, and the most striking pieces have hand-painted flowers. Bases of this pattern all have concentric circles, with large petal swirls to the rim edge, and edges are slightly scalloped.

ROW II—1. *Petal Swirl* covered candy dish, footed base, scarce.
    2. *Petal Swirl* large centerpiece bowl, tab handles.
    3. Footed creamer, hand decorated with enameled flowers.

ROW III—First three items are *Swirled Big Rib*.

ROW III—1. Covered candy bowl, medium mint green.
    2. Footed stem sherbet, true pink.
    3. Salt and pepper shakers, true pink.
    4. *Petal Swirl* double candleholder, true pink.

ROW IV—1. *Swirled Big Rib* 8″ luncheon plate, medium mint green.
    2. Grape leaf salt dip, poor quality, medium green.
    3. *Swirled Big Rib* sandwich server, medium mint green, scarce.
    4. *Swirled Big Rib* consommé, pale pink.

PLATE TWENTY-FOUR

Block and its Variants. *Block* and all its variants, made by every company, were produced in all colors, with the exception of burgundy and cobalt. *Block* is average quality glass and, because of the many colors, can always be used as a fill-in for other patterns. Accessory pieces come in as many different shapes as there are colors. The items vary from shell thin to quite heavy glass.

ROW   I—1. *Tiered Block* candleholder, bright mint green, heavy glass.

      2. Lemon yellow *Block* sherbet, shell thin.

      3. *Block* footed tumbler, 6″, medium mint green, shell thin.

      4 & 5. *Block on Block* matching creamer and sugar, true pink.

ROW II—1. *Block with Rayed Center (not Block with Snowflake)* 9½″ plate, medium mint green.

      2. *Block* ice bucket, wire handle, bright mint green, heavy glass.

      3. *Block with Windmill* 9″ plate, light mint green, poor quality.

ROW III—1. *Block* salt shaker, light mint green.

      2. Footed cone-shaped sugar bowl, *Block* with flared edge.

      3. *Block with Rose* cup and saucer, rose on saucer only. Note cup has flared edge as do the creamer and sugar on either side of it. None of the other *Block* patterns have flared edges.

      4. *Block* creamer, flared edge, matches #2.

      5. *Block* juice tumbler, 4″, pale true pink. All *Block* pink seems to be very pale.

ROW IV—1. Heavy *Block* goblet, 6″, bright mint green.

      2 & 3. *Block* decanter, 7½″, and matching ribbed jigger (original set).

      4. *Block* zig-zag salt shaker, light mint green.

      5. Squatty, low *Block* covered candy bowl, bright mint green.